100 SOLOS
CELLO

Arranged by Ramonn Kraber.

WISE PUBLICATIONS
LONDON/NEW YORK/SYDNEY/COLOGNE

Exclusive Distributors:
Music Sales Limited
8/9 Frith Street, London W1V 5TZ, England
Music Sales Pty. Limited
120 Rothschild Avenue, Rosebery, NSW 2018, Australia

BOOK DESIGN BY PEARCE MARCHBANK STUDIO

Scarborough Fair

Traditional.

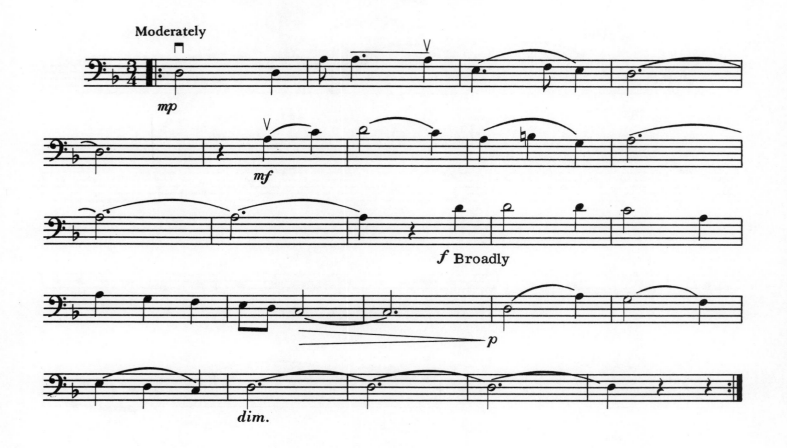

Now Is The Month Of Maying

By Thomas Morley.

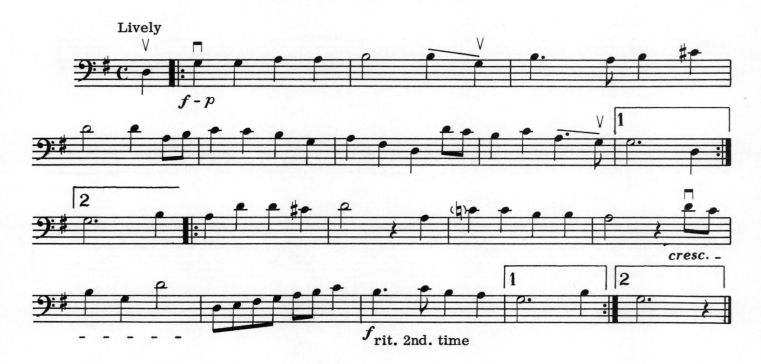

Arrivederci Roma

Words by Garinei and Giovannini. Music by Renato Rascel.
English lyric by Carl Sigman.

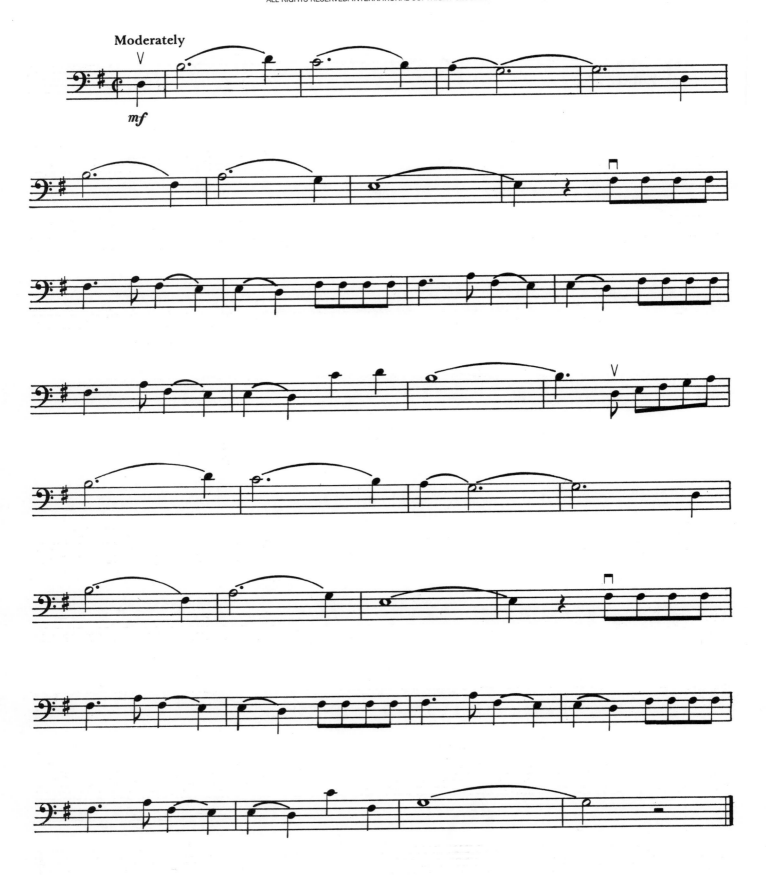

4

Where Have All The Flowers Gone

Words and Music by Pete Seeger.

Edelweiss

Words by Oscar Hammerstein II. Music by Richard Rodgers.

Smile

Words by John Turner and Geoffrey Parsons. Music by Charles Chaplin.

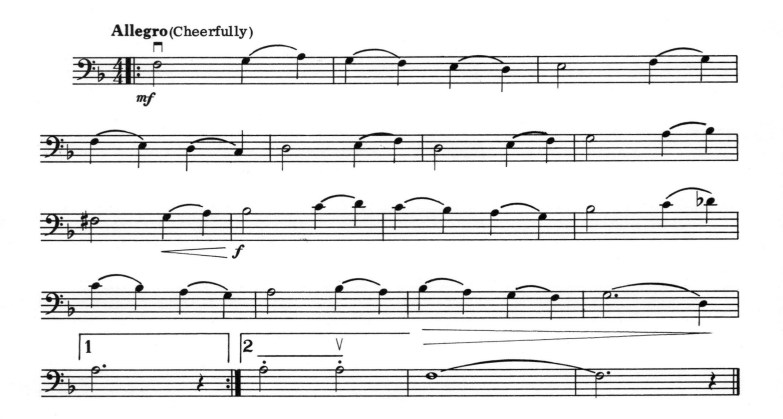

Love Me Tender

Words and Music by Elvis Presley and Vera Matson.

Be My Love

Words by Sammy Cahn. Music by Nicholas Brodszky.

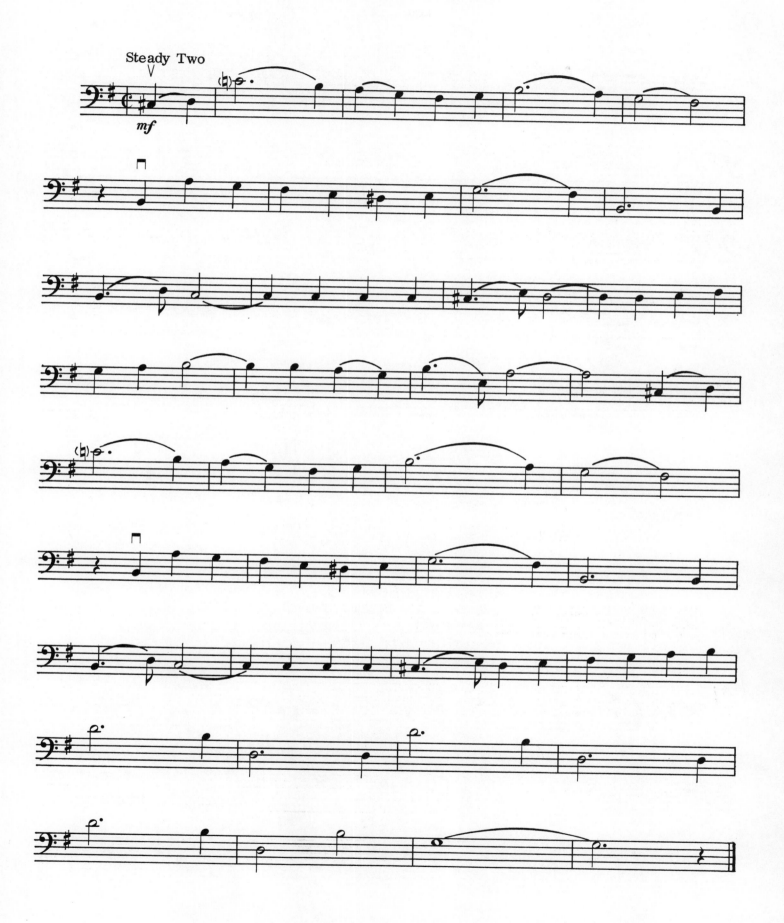

Sailing
Words and Music by Gavin Sutherland.

Mary's Boy Child
Words and Music by Jester Hairston.

Love Is A Song
Words by Larry Morey. Music by Frank Churchill.

The Ballad Of Davy Crockett
Words by Tom Blackburn. Music by George Bruns.

Strangers In The Night

Words by Charles Singleton and Eddie Snyder. Music by Bert Kaempfert.

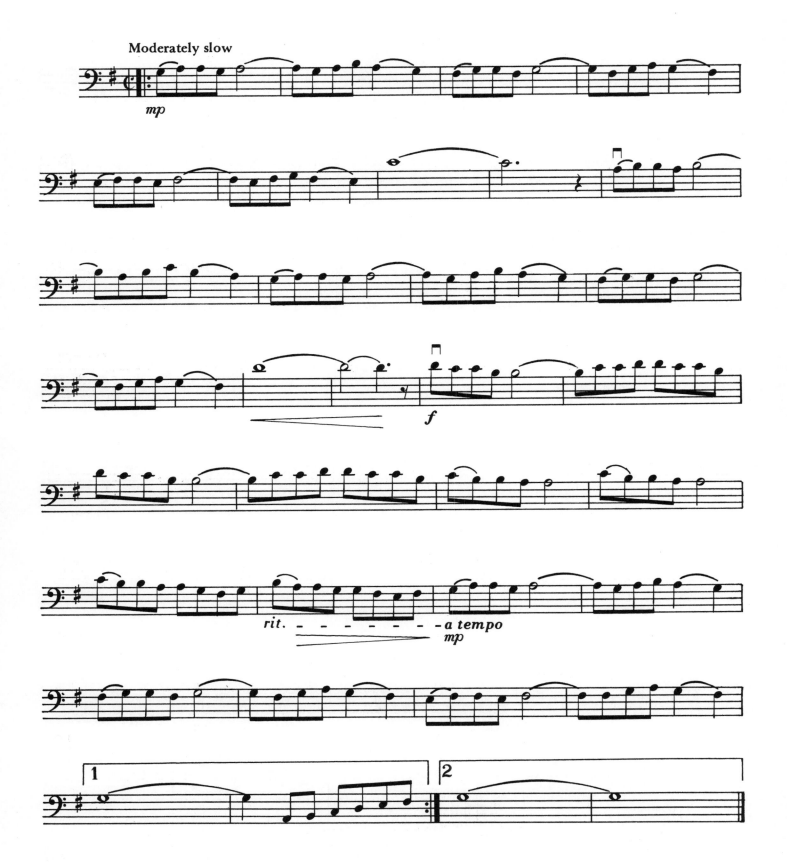

Country Dance
by Ludwig Van Beethoven.

Birdie Song/Birdie Dance
Words and Music by Werner Thomas and Terry Rendall.

Mexican Hat Dance
Traditional.

If I Were A Rich Man

Words by Sheldon Harnick. Music by Jerry Bock.

White Rose of Athens

Words by Norman Newell. Additional Words by Archie Bleyer. Music by Manos Hadjidakis.

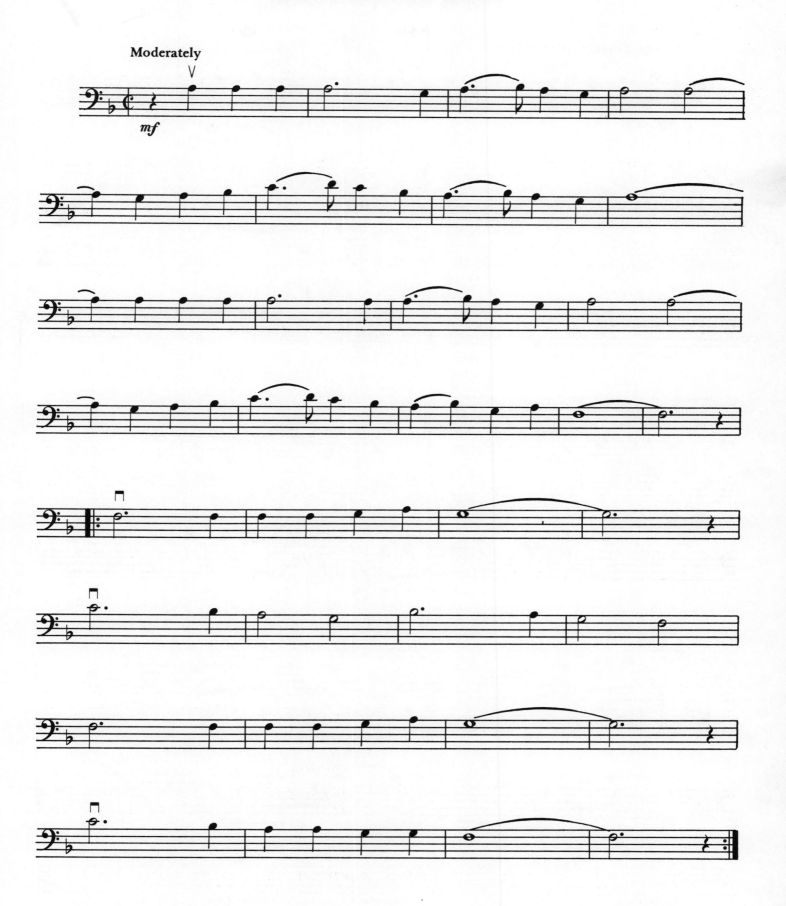

As Long As He Needs Me

Words and Music by Lionel Bart.

Steady Four (Sentimentally)

Paper Roses

Words by Janice Torre. Music by Fred Spielman.

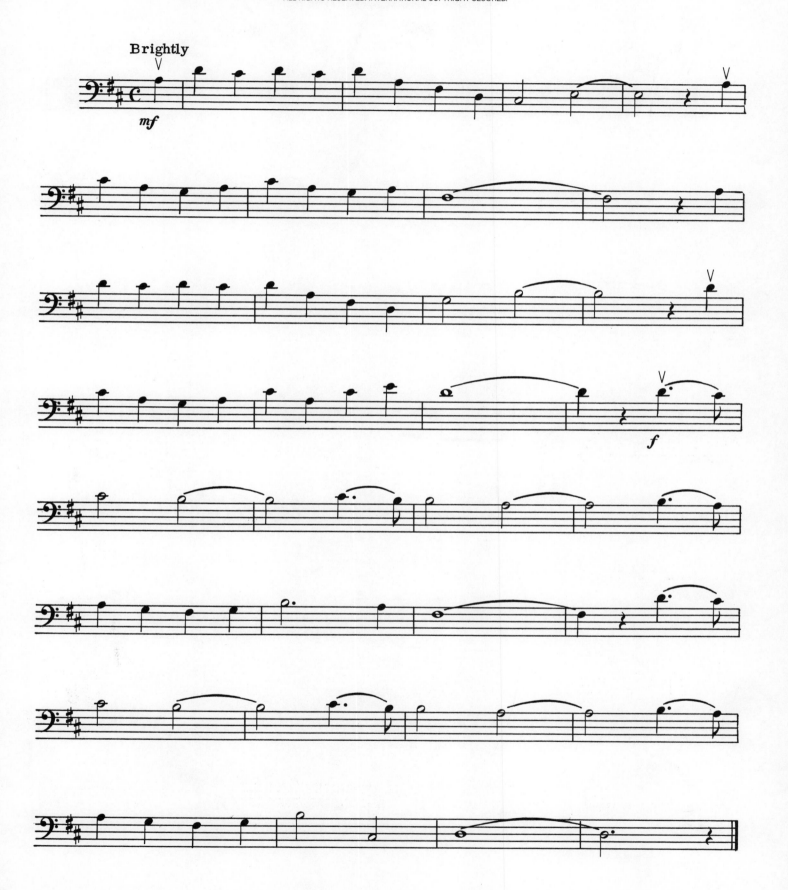

Hawaii Five-O
By Mort Stevens.

When I'm Sixty Four

Words and Music by John Lennon and Paul McCartney.

The Happy Farmer

Traditional.

19

Telstar

by Joe Meek.

Gavotte
By François Gossec.

Tulips From Amsterdam

English Words by Gene Martyn. Original Words by Neumann and Bader.
Music: Ralf Arnie.

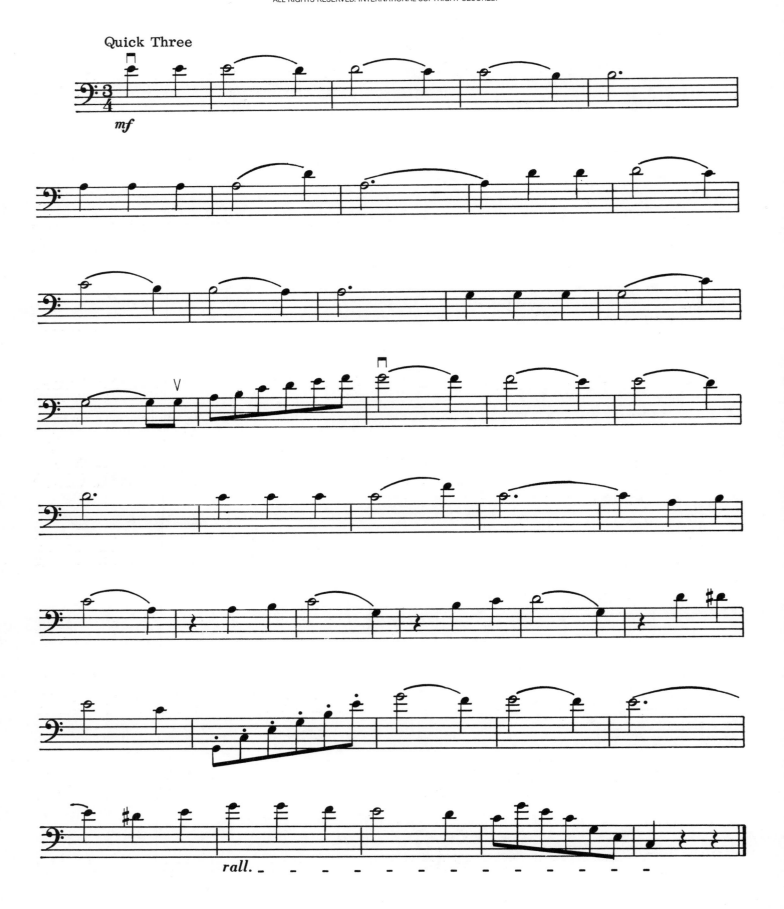

She Loves You

Words and Music by John Lennon and Paul McCartney.

The Very Thought Of You

Words and Music by Ray Noble.

Don't Cry For Me Argentina

Music by Andrew Lloyd Webber. Lyrics by Tim Rice.

Michelle
Words and Music by John Lennon and Paul McCartney.

He's A Tramp

Words and Music by Peggy Lee and Sonny Burke.

Lavender Blue
Traditional.

All My Loving

Words and Music by John Lennon and Paul McCartney.

Slow and sentimental

Annie's Song
Words and Music by John Denver.

Gentle Waltz Tempo

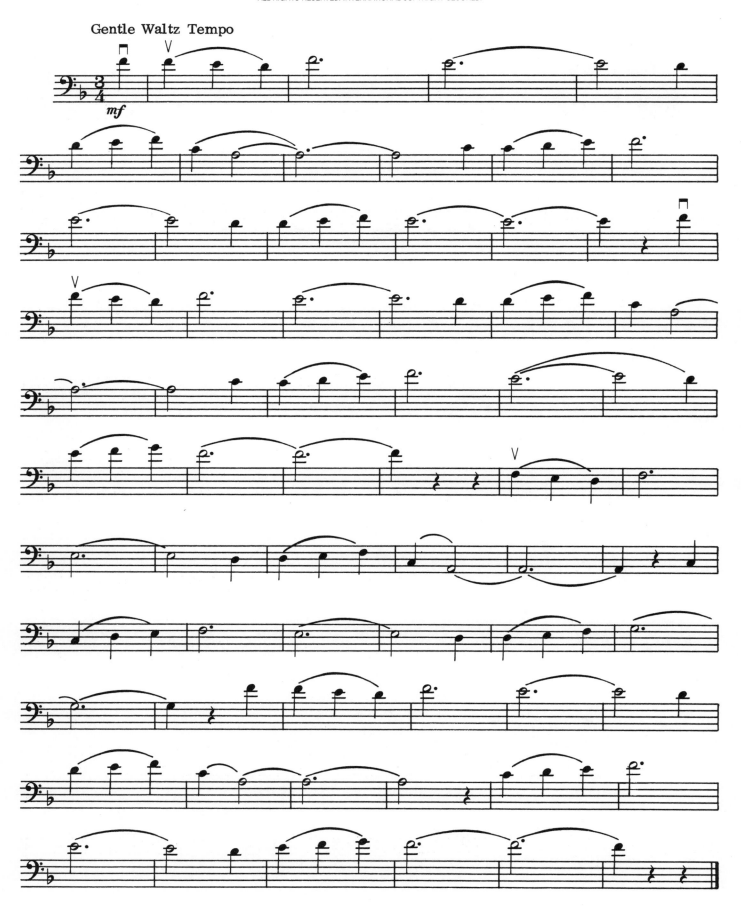

Put Your Head On My Shoulder
Words and Music by Paul Anka.

The Deadwood Stage (Whip-Crack-Away)

Words by Paul Francis Webster. Music by Sammy Fain.

Soldier's Joy
Traditional.

Devil Amongst The Tailors
Traditional.

Downtown

Words and Music by Tony Hatch.

I'd Like To Teach The World To Sing

Words and Music by Roger Cook, Roger Greenaway,
Billy Backer and Billy Davis.

Nymphs And Shepherds

by Henry Purcell.

You Belong To My Heart (Solamente Una Vez)

English lyric by Ray Gilbert. Music and Spanish words by Agustin Lara.

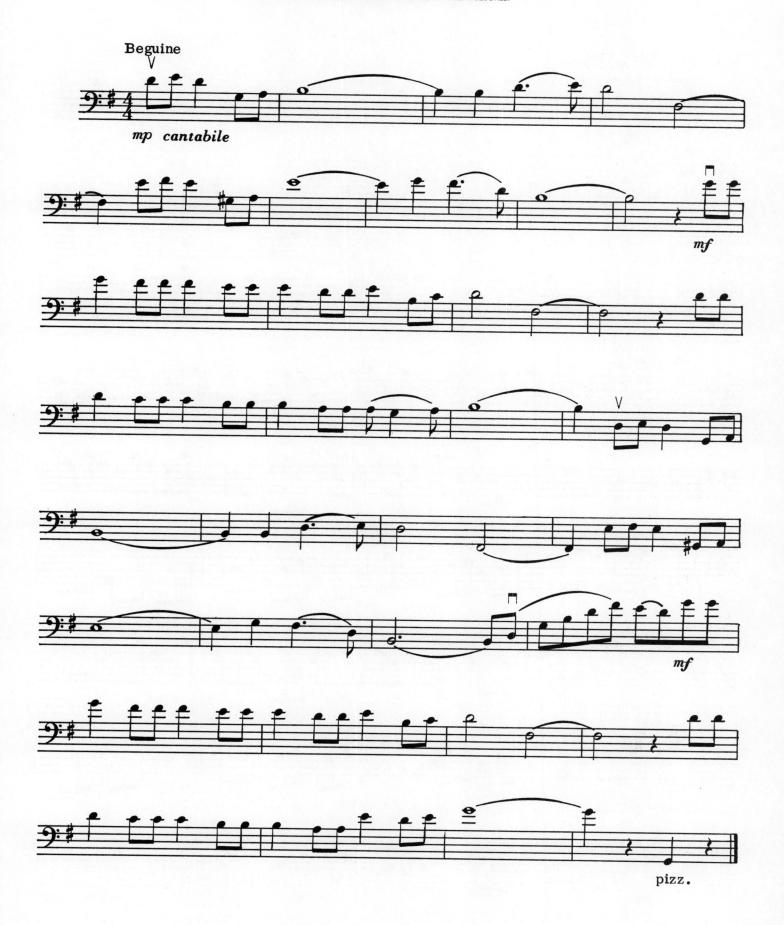

Little Boxes

Words and Music by Malvina Reynolds.

The Surrey With The Fringe On Top
Words by Oscar Hammerstein II. Music by Richard Rodgers.

Yellow Submarine

Words and Music by John Lennon and Paul McCartney.

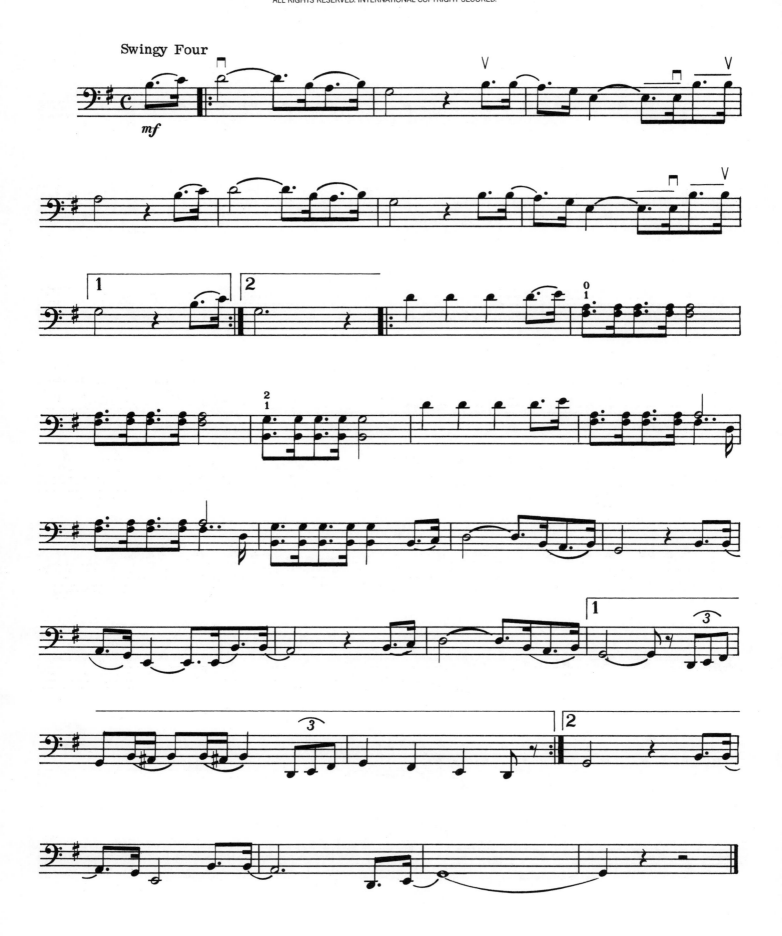

All The Way

Words by Sammy Cahn. Music by James Van Heusen.

Oh Look At Me Now

Words by John DeVries. Music by Joe Bushkin.

Some Enchanted Evening

Words by Oscar Hammerstein II. Music by Richard Rodgers.

Let's Twist Again

Words and Music by Kal Mann and Dave Appell.

Tennessee Waltz
Words and Music by Redd Stewart and Pee Wee King.

Top Of The World

Words by John Bettis. Music by Richard Carpenter.

Romeo And Juliet (Theme From)
By Peter Ilyich Tchaikovsky.

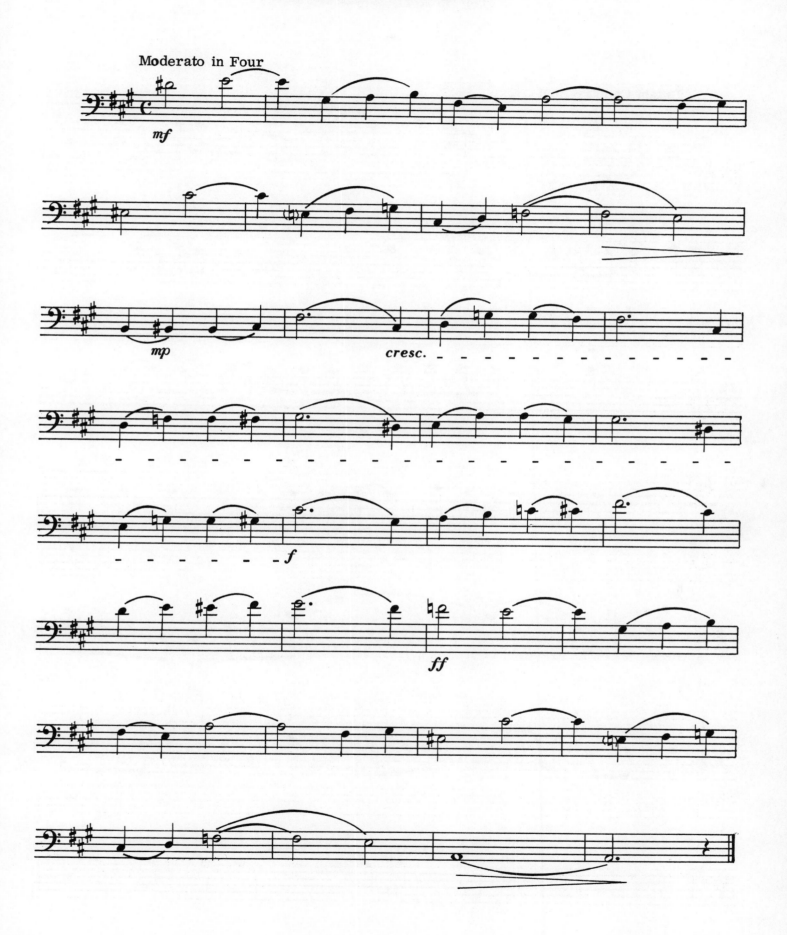

Sweet Sweet Smile

Words and Music by Juice Newton and Otha Young.

I Don't Know How To Love Him

Music by Andrew Lloyd Webber. Lyrics by Tim Rice.

Harmonic
D String

The Hawaiian Wedding Song
Music and Original Hawaiian Lyric by Charles E. King.
English Lyric by Al Hoffman and Dick Manning.

Getting To Know You

Words by Oscar Hammerstein II. Music by Richard Rodgers.

Can't Buy Me Love

Words and Music by John Lennon and Paul McCartney.

It's Magic

Words by Sammy Cahn. Music by Jule Styne.

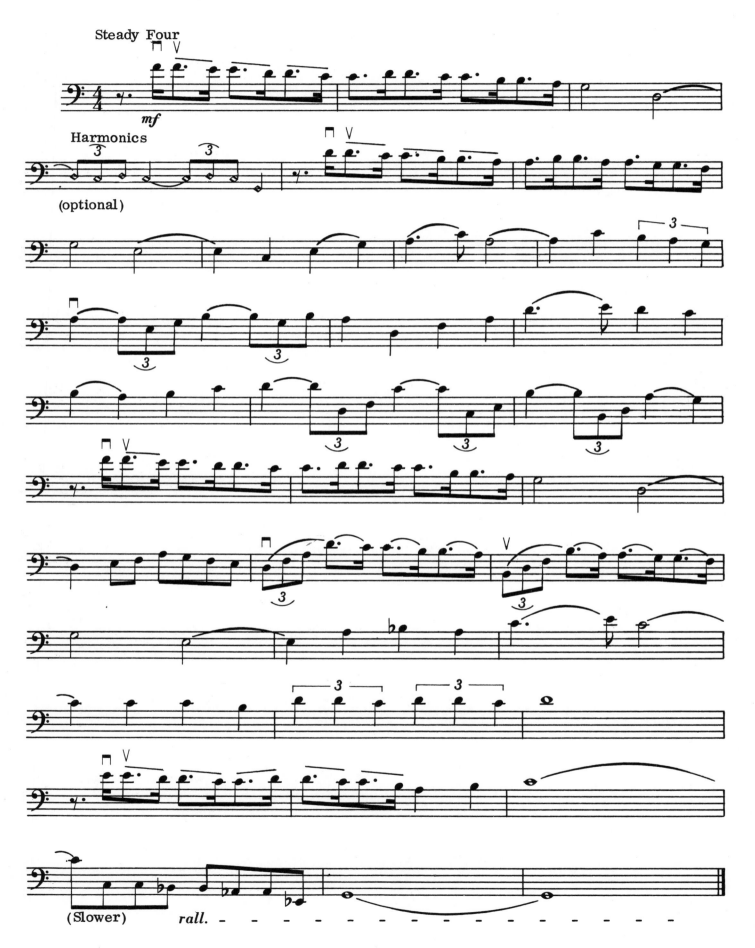

Penny Lane

Words and Music by John Lennon and Paul McCartney.

Among My Souvenirs

Words by Edgar Leslie. Music by Horatio Nicholls.

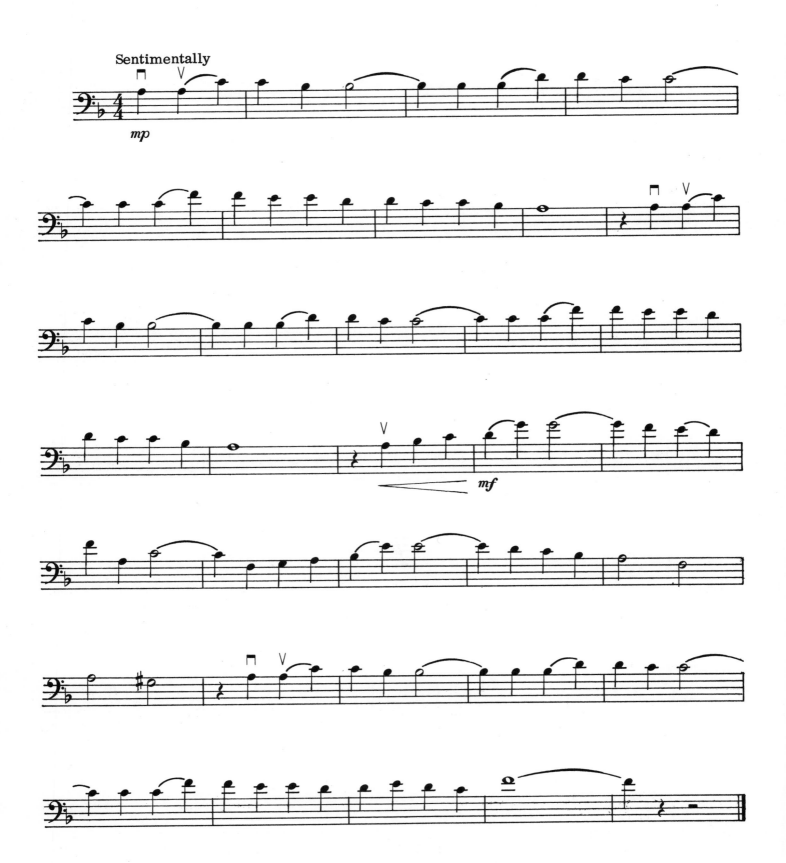

Trains And Boats And Planes

Words by Hal David. Music by Burt Bacharach.

There Is Nothin' Like A Dame

Words by Oscar Hammerstein II. Music by Richard Rodgers.

poco   a   poco   cresc.

Speed The Plough

Traditional.

Fast (Country Style)

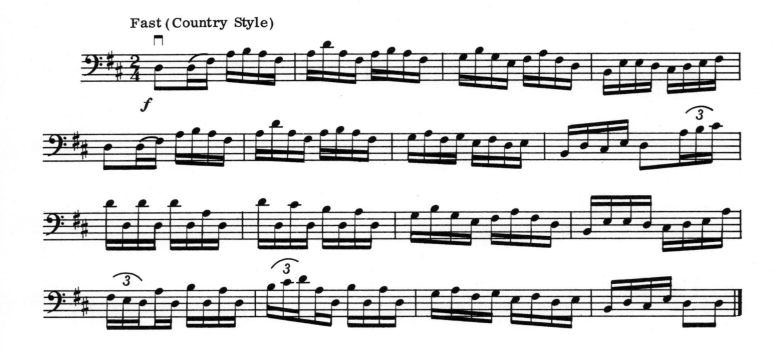

Irish Washerwoman

Traditional.

Fairly Quick Two

Under The Bridges Of Paris (Sous Les Ponts De Paris)
Music by Vincent Scotto. French lyric by J. Rodor.
English lyric by Dorcas Cochran.

Popcorn
By Gershon Kingsley.

Baby It's Cold Outside
Words and Music by Frank Loésser.

Without A Song

Words by William Rose and Edward Eliscu. Music by Vincent Youmans.

Do-Re-Mi
Words by Oscar Hammerstein II. Music by Richard Rodgers

What A Wonderful World

Words and Music by George David Weiss and Bob Thiele.

Chitty Chitty Bang Bang

Words and Music by Richard M. Sherman and Robert B. Sherman.

Minuet
By Franz Joseph Haydn.

There's A Whole Lot Of Loving
Words and Music by Chris Arnold, David Martin and Geoff Morrow.

Taboo

Words by S. K. Russell. Spanish Words and Music by Margarita Lecuona.

Minuet in 'G'
By Ludwig Van Beethoven.

Time's A-Wastin'

Words and Music by Duke Ellington, Mercer Ellington and Don George.

Countrywise
by Ludwig Van Beethoven.

La Cucaracha
Traditional.

Time On My Hands
Words by Harold Adamson and Mack Gordon. Music by Vincent Youmans.

Minuet

By Wolfgang Amadeus Mozart.

Basin Street Blues

Words and Music by Spencer Williams.

These Foolish Things

Words by Eric Maschwitz. Music by Jack Strachey.

Try A Little Tenderness

Words and Music by Harry Woods, Jimmy Campbell and Reg Connelly.

Cabaret

Music by John Kander. Lyrics by Fred Ebb.

Perdido

Words by Harry Lenk and Ervin Drake. Music by Juan Tizol.

Lullaby Of Birdland
Words by George David Weiss. Music by George Shearing.

Bibbidi-Bobbidi-Boo

Words by Jerry Livingston. Music by Mack David and Al Hoffman.

Don't Worry 'Bout Me

Words by Ted Koehler. Music by Rube Bloom.

The Entertainer

By Scott Joplin.

The Coffee Song
Words and Music by Bob Hilliard and Dick Miles.

Turkey In The Straw

Traditional.

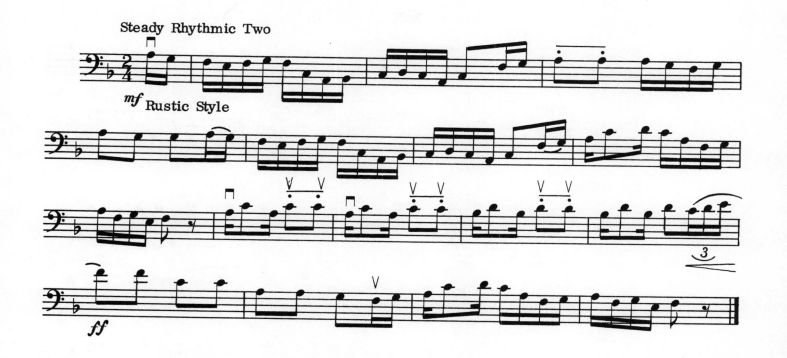

My Darling, My Darling

Words and Music by Frank Loesser.

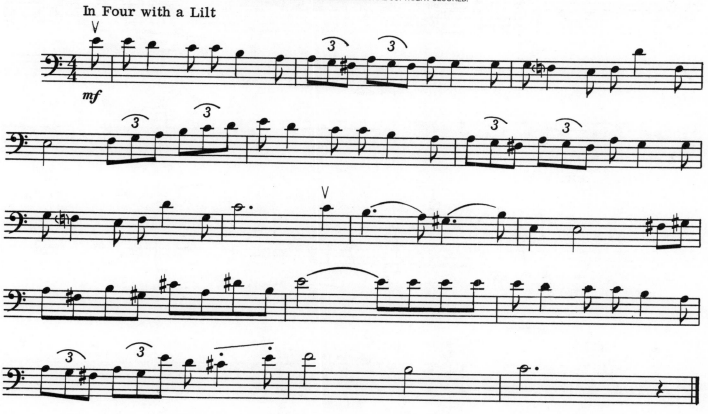

Memories Are Made Of This

Words and Music by Terry Gilkyson, Richard Dehr and Frank Miller.

Under Paris Skies (Sous Le Ciel De Paris)

Words by Kim Gannon. Music by Hubert Giraud.

Yesterday

Words and Music by John Lennon and Paul McCartney.

Better Love Next Time

Words and Music by Steve Pippin, Johnny Slate and Larry Keith.

Humoresque
by Antonin Dvořák.

Honeysuckle Rose

Words by Andy Razaf. Music by Thomas 'Fats' Waller.

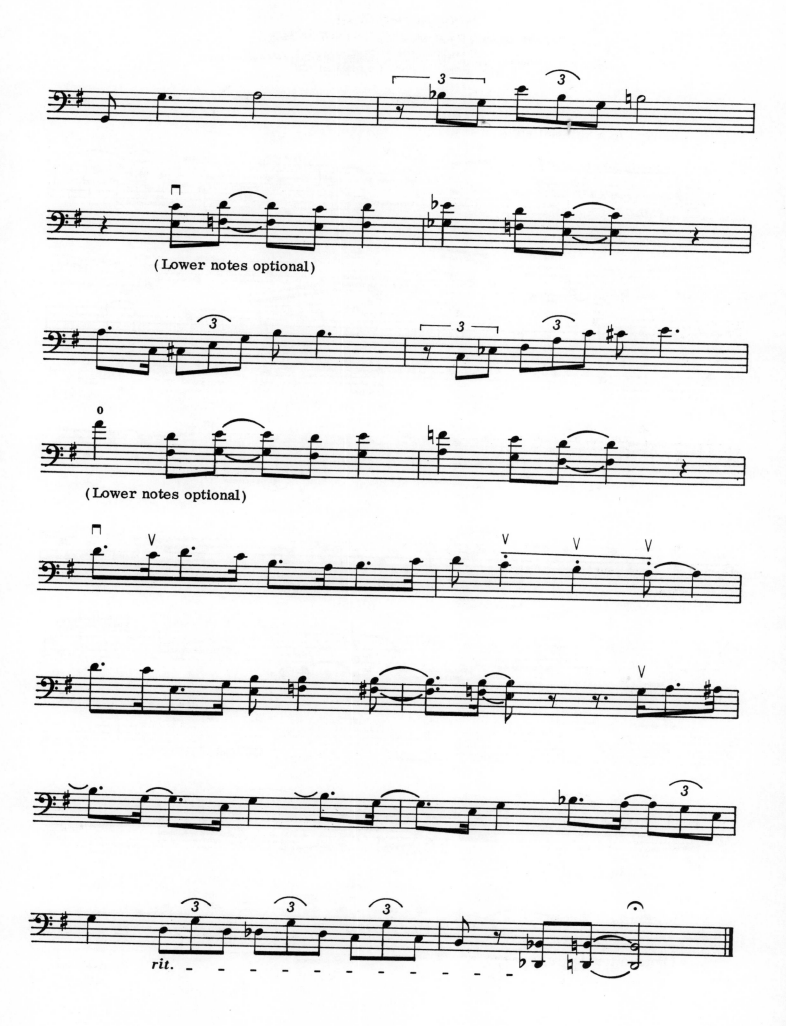

(Lower notes optional)

(Lower notes optional)

rit.

Sweet Sue—Just You

Words by Will J. Harris. Music by Victor Young.

103

Stormy Weather
Words by Ted Koehler. Music by Harold Arlen.

Printed by J. B. Offset (Marks Tey) Limited, Colchester, Essex.

12551 10/91